Crescent Moon Cat

by Roxi Mathis

based on a spontaneous song by Dan Mathis

and of course,

dedicated to Dan

I am a crescent moon cat.

I want
your food
So I can
be fat.

It's my greatest desire to grow and expand.

To achieve a size that is
decidedly out of hand.

Tremendous expansion!
To the size of a mansion!

A giant kitty!
As big as a city!

I want to get as big as a mountain.

CRUNCH! MUNCH! SIP! SMACK!

Heftiness will be the outcome!

Bigger and bigger,
until I can make my launch

Above the sky, beyond this place

Past the clouds
out OUT into space!

Then I can learn
the rhythm of
the galaxies

SPIN! SWOOP!
CRASH! BANG!

Plunge right in!
No guarantees!

I'll stroll along the edge of light

Eating asteroids and comets for food.

Nudging planets aside
to accommodate for my magnitude

I'll be the biggest thing in all existence.
Hardly to be believed,
Spanning an improbable distance.

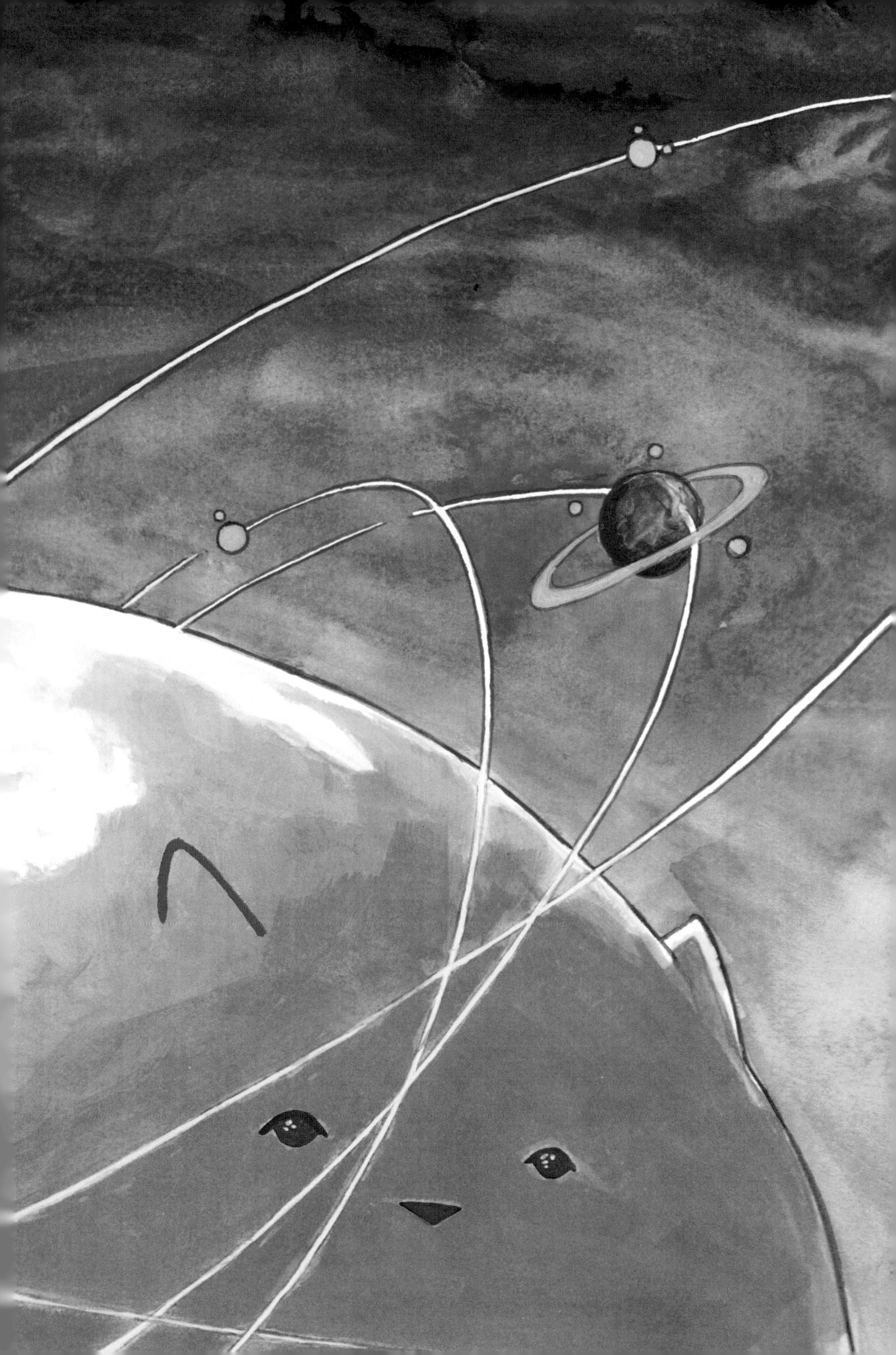

And when I can expand no more,
when my weight is pressed
against the cosmic door,

That's when I make the change!
That's when I extend my range!

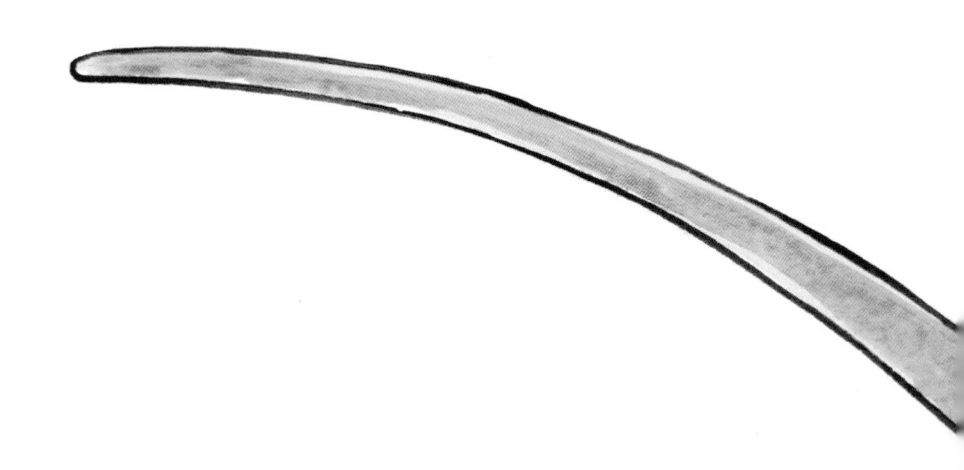

Into the beyond beyond
Into the unknown unknown

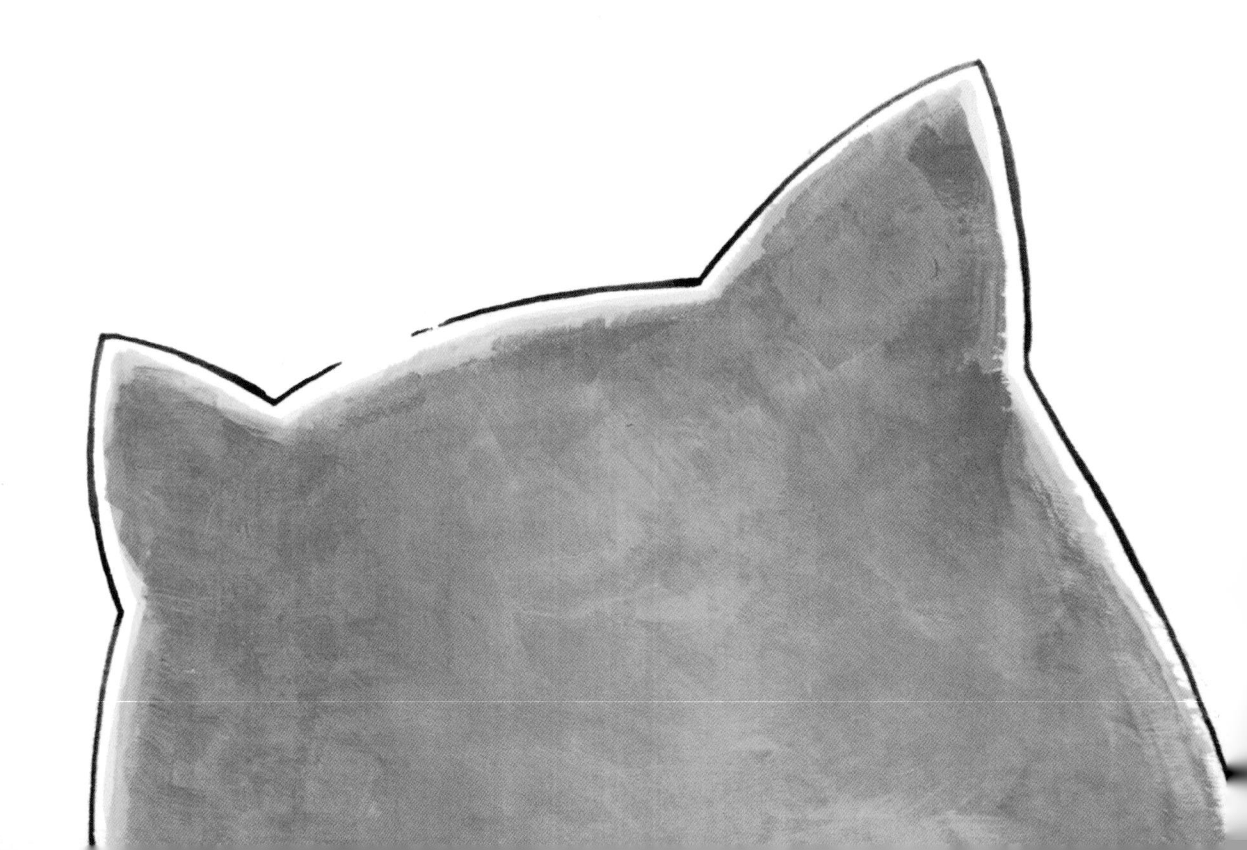

To learn what we don't know
that we don't know we don't know

and what then?

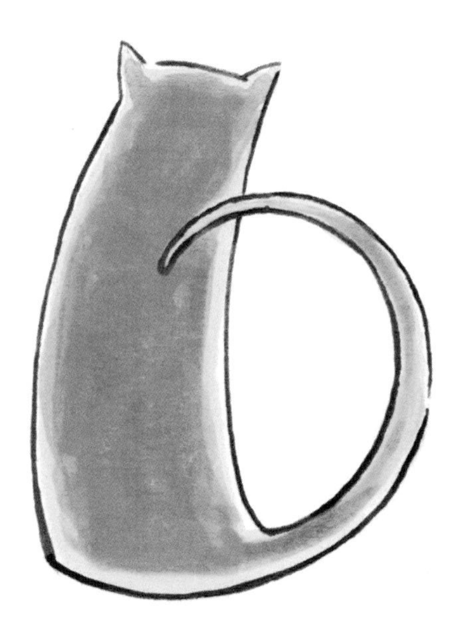

well I don't know...

But what I do know
is that before I can go beyond,
before I can get into space,
before I can go where I belong...

I need your food.
So I can be fat.

Because I am still
a crescent moon cat.

The end.

Made in the USA
Monee, IL
18 February 2022

90815146R00021